The Great Snakeskin

John Agard

Illustrated by
Jill Newton

Series Editors
Steve Barlow and Steve Skidmore

The Great Snakeskin

This is what the author, John Agard, says about this play.

The Great Snakeskin was inspired by an old Amerindian legend. I got to know about it through a book of legends told by the Amerindians of Guyana, the country where I was born and grew up.

As for the birds and the watersnake, you may get into the spirit of their characters by thinking of certain people you know. I remember seeing a programme once about the famous actor Alec Guinness, who said that whenever he was having difficulty with a part he would visit the zoo for ideas. Once he was playing the part of an aristocratic gentleman, and it all came together when he watched the penguins walking around in their black and white frock coats. So why don't you do the opposite, and observe the way people talk and move in order to help you get into the characters of the birds and the snake.

Harpy Eagle, for instance, is a large and powerful bird of prey. He is very noble and proud. He feels no need to show off or go around boasting about his strength. But don't push him.

Parrot is what we in the Caribbean call 'full of mouth' — the kind of person who would talk himself out of a difficult situation.

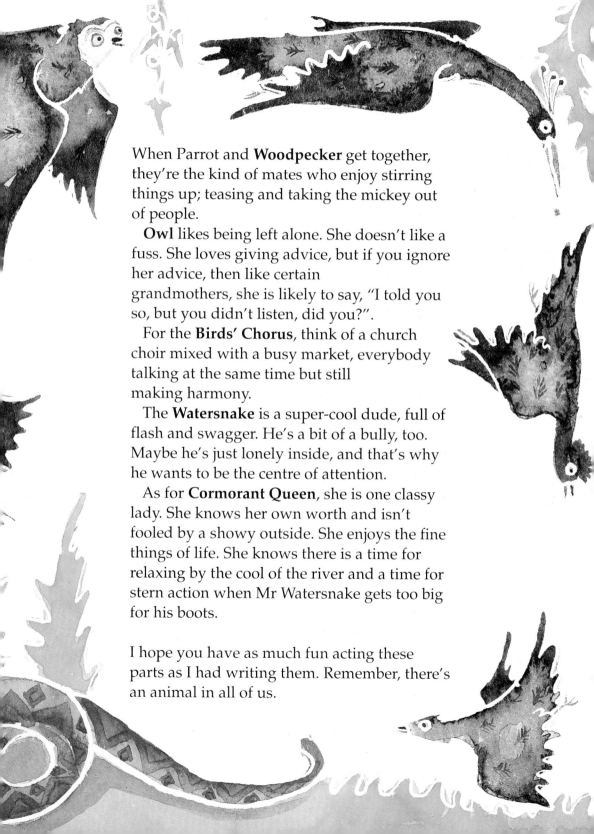

When Parrot and **Woodpecker** get together, they're the kind of mates who enjoy stirring things up; teasing and taking the mickey out of people.

Owl likes being left alone. She doesn't like a fuss. She loves giving advice, but if you ignore her advice, then like certain grandmothers, she is likely to say, "I told you so, but you didn't listen, did you?".

For the **Birds' Chorus**, think of a church choir mixed with a busy market, everybody talking at the same time but still making harmony.

The **Watersnake** is a super-cool dude, full of flash and swagger. He's a bit of a bully, too. Maybe he's just lonely inside, and that's why he wants to be the centre of attention.

As for **Cormorant Queen**, she is one classy lady. She knows her own worth and isn't fooled by a showy outside. She enjoys the fine things of life. She knows there is a time for relaxing by the cool of the river and a time for stern action when Mr Watersnake gets too big for his boots.

I hope you have as much fun acting these parts as I had writing them. Remember, there's an animal in all of us.

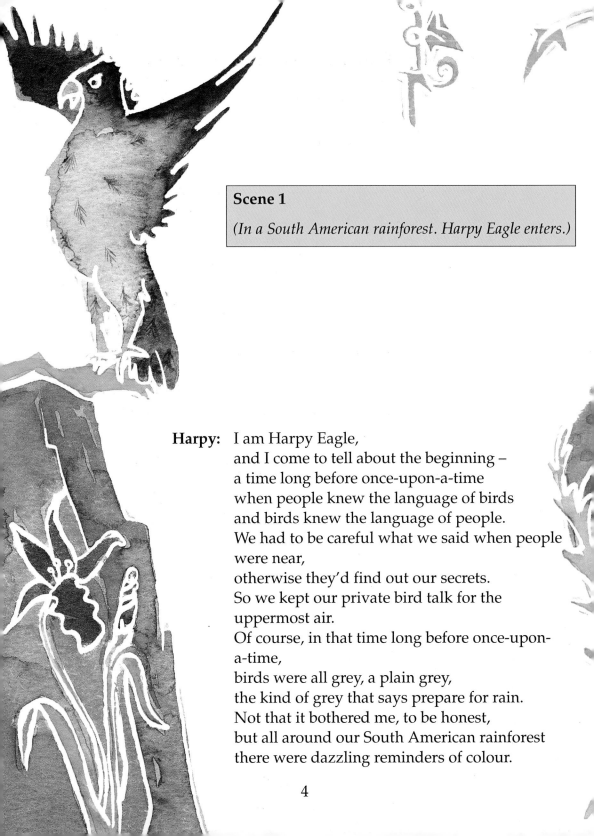

Scene 1

(In a South American rainforest. Harpy Eagle enters.)

Harpy: I am Harpy Eagle,
and I come to tell about the beginning –
a time long before once-upon-a-time
when people knew the language of birds
and birds knew the language of people.
We had to be careful what we said when people
were near,
otherwise they'd find out our secrets.
So we kept our private bird talk for the
uppermost air.
Of course, in that time long before once-upon-
a-time,
birds were all grey, a plain grey,
the kind of grey that says prepare for rain.
Not that it bothered me, to be honest,
but all around our South American rainforest
there were dazzling reminders of colour.

4

Harpy: Trees had a generous share of green.
Sky was brightest blue. Sun was dazzling yellow.
As for Rainbow, I won't even attempt to describe Rainbow.
Some of the animals were always having a go at us, with our grey feathers.

Jaguar made a big thing of his spotted skin.
Marmoset monkey was always showing off her fur of gold.
Even Frog kept drawing attention to himself,
as if we feathered folk couldn't recognize a little lump of green.
Now why would I want to give up my towering rock
and take up residence in a slimy pool?
I suppose they'd say I was jealous,
but frankly, I couldn't see the reason for the fuss.
Can you hear all that fuss they're making?

(Harpy goes to his rock. The other birds appear on stage and do a dance, making bird noises.)

Birds' Chorus: We happy to fly, we happy to fly,
but we'd be telling a lie, telling a lie
to say we happy to be grey.
No, grey isn't the way we'd like to stay.

O it isn't fair, it isn't fair,
to be grey, to be grey
in a world of colour everywhere.
No, grey isn't the way we'd like to stay.

(Birds take up positions, each saying his or her piece.)

Toucan: I need no introduction I think.
I'm Toucan of the big-big beak.
But I'd exchange it any day
for a touch of yellow or pink.

Cock-of-the-Rock: *(Dancing on rock)*
I Cock-of-the-Rock
can dance
can prance
can preen
for my queen.
But oh for a touch
of orange or green.

Woodpecker: I keep taptap heartbeat
taptap honeybeak
taptap honeybeak
But I do feel
a little colour would make
Woodpecker look taptap sweet.

Kiskadee: I quite like
the sound of my voice.
I think it suits me.
Kiskadeeee!
But grey won't be my choice
for Kiskadee.
Kiskadeeeee!

Parrot: Who can can talk
Who can can squawk
Repeat words
Best of all birds?
Yours truly Parrot.
But how I pray
for a bit
of colour
to match my sparkling wit.
Anything but grey!
Anything but grey!
Anything but grey!

Owl: All right, Parrot, you've had your say.
In daytime it doesn't matter either way.
But at night when Moon shines bright
I sometimes think yellow on Owl would be right.

Hummingbird: *(Showing flying skills)*
Forwards, backwards
I make flying seem easy,
wings beating faster
than eye can see.
Like a tiny rainbow –
that's how Hummingbird
ought to glow.

Harpy: *(To audience)*
Colour for some might be all right.
But personally speaking, I rather keep my might.

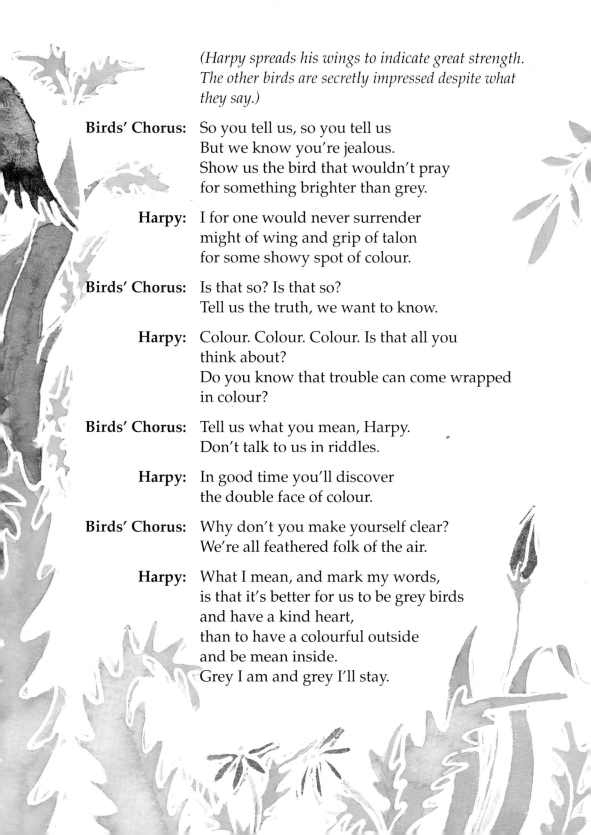

*(Harpy spreads his wings to indicate great strength.
The other birds are secretly impressed despite what
they say.)*

Birds' Chorus: So you tell us, so you tell us
But we know you're jealous.
Show us the bird that wouldn't pray
for something brighter than grey.

Harpy: I for one would never surrender
might of wing and grip of talon
for some showy spot of colour.

Birds' Chorus: Is that so? Is that so?
Tell us the truth, we want to know.

Harpy: Colour. Colour. Colour. Is that all you
think about?
Do you know that trouble can come wrapped
in colour?

Birds' Chorus: Tell us what you mean, Harpy.
Don't talk to us in riddles.

Harpy: In good time you'll discover
the double face of colour.

Birds' Chorus: Why don't you make yourself clear?
We're all feathered folk of the air.

Harpy: What I mean, and mark my words,
is that it's better for us to be grey birds
and have a kind heart,
than to have a colourful outside
and be mean inside.
Grey I am and grey I'll stay.

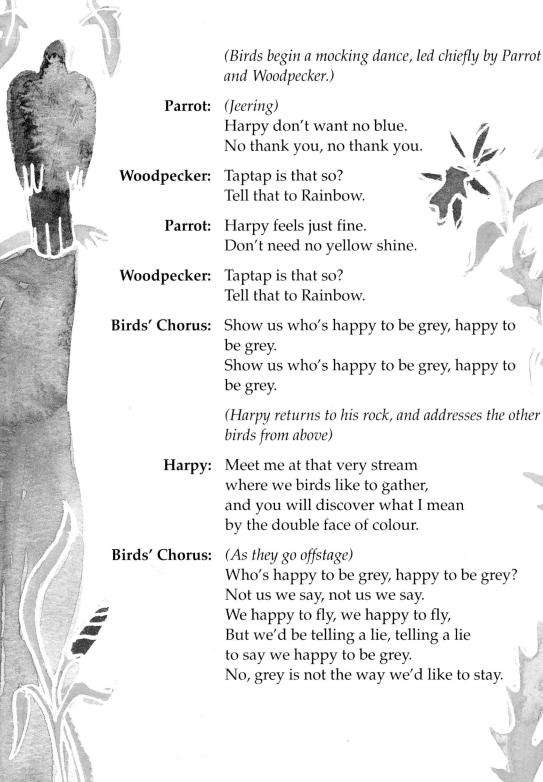

(Birds begin a mocking dance, led chiefly by Parrot and Woodpecker.)

Parrot: *(Jeering)*
Harpy don't want no blue.
No thank you, no thank you.

Woodpecker: Taptap is that so?
Tell that to Rainbow.

Parrot: Harpy feels just fine.
Don't need no yellow shine.

Woodpecker: Taptap is that so?
Tell that to Rainbow.

Birds' Chorus: Show us who's happy to be grey, happy to
be grey.
Show us who's happy to be grey, happy to
be grey.

(Harpy returns to his rock, and addresses the other birds from above)

Harpy: Meet me at that very stream
where we birds like to gather,
and you will discover what I mean
by the double face of colour.

Birds' Chorus: *(As they go offstage)*
Who's happy to be grey, happy to be grey?
Not us we say, not us we say.
We happy to fly, we happy to fly,
But we'd be telling a lie, telling a lie
to say we happy to be grey.
No, grey is not the way we'd like to stay.

Scene 2

(By a stream. For the moment the stream is peaceful, but then a plaintive South American Indian flute is heard, giving way to a sudden frightening stirring of the water from which emerges the Great Watersnake with much hissing. Harpy is already on stage, but the Great Watersnake cannot see him.)

Watersnake: I am the Great Watersnake.
Strikingly handsome, as you can see.
My skin is the smartest, the sleekest
in this entire rainforest.
Even though I am by nature modest
I'd say my skin was simply the best.
In fact, without overstretching the point,
I'd say Rainbow must envy my belly.
As for those birds in their plain grey,
why don't they come on out and make my day?

(Watersnake breaks into a snake dance to demonstrate the splendour of his skin as well as his mean intentions.)

Watersnake: Whenever those birds come near
I will fill their little hearts with fear.
O what a hissing hissing joke for me
to give their grey feathers the trembles.

Watersnake: I happen to know that this is their
favourite stream
where they like to sip and dip and dream
when they're tired of moaning about their grey.
Well, I'll soon put an end to all that.
No more sitting around on the banks of
this stream.
Oh no. I intend to make it mine and mine alone.

From now on, this stream will be my home,
my personal playground for slithering around.
The sort of place where a watersnake can
really unwind.
But I think I hear those birds coming.
Soon they'll start singing their usual number.
I'll just lie still, as if I'm dead
or in the middle of a midday slumber.

*(Birds enter. Startled by the sight of Watersnake, they
keep a cautious distance. Then, enticed by his stillness
and wondrous skin, they timidly draw nearer.)*

Birds' Chorus: No, this cannot be, our eyes must be
playing tricks.
We're never seen so many colours all in
one place.
Is this a magical creature from outer space?

12

Hummingbird: A rainbow lying on the ground!
What a sight to behold!

Toucan: Brighter than Marmoset's gold.

Parrot: *(Repeats)* Brighter than Marmoset's gold.

Cock-of-the-Rock: Greener than Iguana's green.

Parrot: *(Repeats)* Greener than Iguana's green.

Woodpecker: Sleeker than Ocelot's spots.

Parrot: *(Repeats)* Sleeker than Ocelot's spots.

Kiskadee: A yellow to outdazzle Sun.

Parrot: *(Repeats)* Outdazzle Sun.

Toucan: A blue to outshimmer Sky and Sea.

Parrot: *(Repeats)* Outshimmer Sky and Sea.

Birds' Chorus: No, this cannot be, this cannot be.

(Watersnake, suddenly slithering upwards with a hiss, sends the birds flurrying away.)

Watersnake: It certainly can be, it certainly can be.
What you see is what you get
and once you see me, you'll regret.
For I am the Great Watersnake,
no figment of your imagination.
So if you know what's good for your feathers,
you birds better start your migration.
This stream isn't big enough for all of us.
No room for grey birds alongside a snake
so fabulous.

(With a terrifying hiss, Watersnake stylishly slithers underwater, and disappears. Silence.)

Harpy: *(To audience)*
Didn't I say that trouble would one day come
wrapped in colour?

Owl: In daylight, as you know, I'm blind,
so I could not see the brightness of this creature
but I could feel evil in his nature.

Toucan: Oh Owl, if only you could have seen his skin.

Hummingbird: Even the tip of his tail was a jewel.

Parrot: *(Repeats)* A jewel.

Cock-of-the-Rock: And did you see those orange spots?

Parrot: *(Repeats)* Orange spots.

Birds' Chorus: There's nothing that can compare
in Water, Land or Air.

Owl: Enough talk about his skin,
and the fine colours you've seen.
Remember this watersnake is mean,
and he has made it perfectly clear
that he doesn't want us near this stream.

Birds' Chorus: Our favourite stream.

Owl: You heard how he struck the water
as if his tail was filled with thunder.

Birds' Chorus: We'd have to fly for miles in search of some creek
to dip our weary wings and beak.

Toucan: And I myself would rather hop than fly.

Birds' Chorus: *(In sad faraway voices)*
No more to dream beside our stream
where the water runs peaceful
where the water runs clean
and all because of one that's wicked and mean
O gone gone the dreaming days.

Owl: Well, all is not lost, we may yet save our stream.
If we put all our thoughts together
we may find a way to slay this monster.
Let's sleep on it.

Birds' Chorus: Yes, let's sleep on it.
We may be grey
and we have no hiss
But things can't go on like this.

We may be grey
but we'll find a way
to slay this monster.
May tomorrow bring an answer.

Parrot: *(Repeats)* Sleep on it. Sleep on it. Sleep on it.

(Birds go off.)

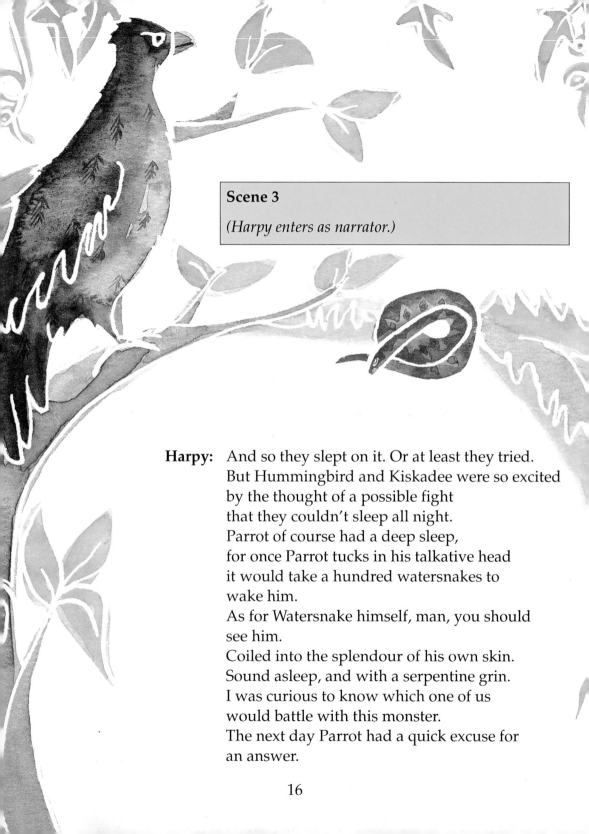

Scene 3

(Harpy enters as narrator.)

Harpy: And so they slept on it. Or at least they tried.
But Hummingbird and Kiskadee were so excited
by the thought of a possible fight
that they couldn't sleep all night.
Parrot of course had a deep sleep,
for once Parrot tucks in his talkative head
it would take a hundred watersnakes to
wake him.
As for Watersnake himself, man, you should
see him.
Coiled into the splendour of his own skin.
Sound asleep, and with a serpentine grin.
I was curious to know which one of us
would battle with this monster.
The next day Parrot had a quick excuse for
an answer.

16

Parrot: I can hurl talk at him.
Talk him out of his skin.
But when it comes to battling,
that's another thing.
I'm not risking my feathers –
not even these grey feathers.

Toucan: I'd gladly peck him with my beak
or try to scare him with a shriek.
I'm a fierce defender of my nest
but with this monster I'd lose the contest.

Cock-of-the-Rock: I'm one for dancing
I'm one for prancing
not for advancing
against a monster.
If I challenge him to a dance
he won't stand a chance.
But …

Hummingbird: Over little flower
see me hover
wings humming, humming, humming,
But I'd fly backwards
as soon as I saw
that monster coming.

Kiskadee: To catch
worm
is easy-easy.
Even Hawk
ain't no match
for Kiskadee
in mid-flight.
But to deal
with one that can slither and bite …

Owl: Well, what can an old bird say?
To challenge this monster by day
Would really be amusing.
I'd be too blind to see him, much less abuse him.
I'd better stick to catching mice
but at least I can offer some advice.

Why don't we birds join together
and make a great rope of vine?
Then Harpy, with his powerful talons,
can swoop down and strangle the demon.
It's only an idea, but Harpy might be willing.

Harpy: *(To audience)*
See what I mean? When it comes to killing
this demon, I knew they'd want me to step in.

Birds' Chorus: Yes, let's ask him, let's ask him.
Come on Harpy, this is the chance to prove
your power.
Please say yes.

Harpy: I have no need to prove my power.
You have seen how Monkey scurry
when my talons flash their fury.

Birds' Chorus: But to rid us of Watersnake, this demon,
our enemy,
will bring you even greater glory.

Harpy: I must agree this watersnake is very greedy.
He wants to take over our favourite stream.
But why can't that stream be shared
by all creatures of land and air?
It is obvious this watersnake
doesn't like the looks of us.
He thinks himself ever so fabulous.
Well, let's show him we're not afraid.
And I have a suggestion.
You know the human expression – Fight fire
with fire?
Well, Harpy says – Fight water with water.
And the best one to deal with Watersnake
is the one who herself lives in the Kingdom
of Water,
and you know who I mean.
That's my good friend, Cormorant Queen.

Birds' Chorus: *(As they go off briskly)*
Well, let's go to Cormorant Queen,
Let's go to Cormorant Queen,
See if she'd face this monster so mean.

Scene 4

(Cormorant Queen sitting on her regal rock. Harpy has got there before the other birds, and is sitting beside her. There is a stream in the background.)

Birds' Chorus: We would like to ask you a favour.
Wicked Watersnake has taken over our stream and we'd like you to kill him …

Harpy: Not so fast, my friends. How about a little courtesy?
Begin with "Good day, Your Majesty."

Birds' Chorus: Good day, Your Majesty.

Cormorant Queen: Why, Harpy, no need for all the formality.

Harpy: *(To audience)*
I tell you, she has no pretty feathers to preen, but she surely talks like a queen.

Cormorant Queen: Well, my high-flying friends of the air,
you certainly took your time getting here.
I've been expecting you.
No need to go into the details.
I've been busy dealing with worms, and eels,
and snails,
But don't think I haven't noticed Watersnake.
The Great Watersnake, as he likes to call himself.

He plans to make a certain stream his
private place.
And that stream, as you know, is very dear to
my heart.
I often lie there with the wind in my face
When I want to get away from quarrelsome
Marmoset monkeys.
That stream soothes my feathers like a
refreshing breeze,
so if Watersnake wants a battle, let battle begin.
We'll soon see if his wits can match his skin.
Harpy, seize me an arrow, the very best the
Indians make.
Time to face the Great Watersnake.

Birds' Chorus: Time to face the Great Watersnake.
But what's the plan, Harpy, what have you
in mind?
Will you attack from the front or behind?

Cormorant Queen: Harpy and I have been thinking a lot
And we have come up with a little plot.
Harpy, with a long and sturdy rope-vine between his talons,
will keep Watersnake occupied.
Then I, Cormorant Queen, in one swift dive
Will send the arrow through the demon's hide.
That will be our strategy.
So my feathered friends, are you ready?

Birds' Chorus: Yes, your Majesty.
Good luck to Cormorant Queen and Harpy.

Scene 5

(By the stream, where Watersnake is relaxing in the sunshine.)

Watersnake: I must say these birds have been lying low.
Are they afraid of my hiss or my slither?

Birds' Chorus: *(In a sudden outburst)*
NEITHER! NEITHER!

(Birds form a circle for the choreographed fight about to begin. Harpy fights Watersnake, waving his rope-vine. Cormorant Queen is hidden, holding an arrow. The other birds cheer Harpy.)

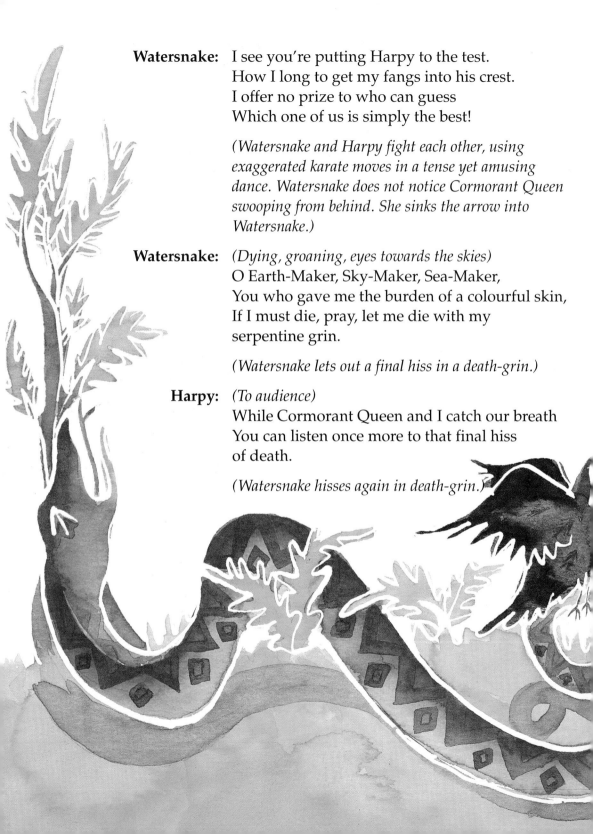

Watersnake: I see you're putting Harpy to the test.
How I long to get my fangs into his crest.
I offer no prize to who can guess
Which one of us is simply the best!

(Watersnake and Harpy fight each other, using exaggerated karate moves in a tense yet amusing dance. Watersnake does not notice Cormorant Queen swooping from behind. She sinks the arrow into Watersnake.)

Watersnake: *(Dying, groaning, eyes towards the skies)*
O Earth-Maker, Sky-Maker, Sea-Maker,
You who gave me the burden of a colourful skin,
If I must die, pray, let me die with my
serpentine grin.

(Watersnake lets out a final hiss in a death-grin.)

Harpy: *(To audience)*
While Cormorant Queen and I catch our breath
You can listen once more to that final hiss
of death.

(Watersnake hisses again in death-grin.)

Birds' Chorus: Long Live Cormorant Queen
Long Live Cormorant Queen
She laid him low with her arrow.
Now let's seize the skin the skin the skin!

(As Harpy speaks, the Cormorant Queen and birds act out what he is saying, lifting off Watersnake's colourful cloak. The Cormorant Queen takes his grey mask. Then the birds fly offstage and return quickly, wearing their own colourful cloaks).

Harpy: Now it is time for Birds to lift away
Watersnake's skin.
Cormorant Queen lifts the snake's head in
her beak.
She gives a sign for the others to join in,
and up go Birds with Watersnake's skin.

25

Harpy: Look at that skin lifted into the air,
each bird carrying his or her little share.

Suddenly, as my grey friends are flapping,
something's started happening!
They can't believe their eyes or feathers,
for what was once grey is now brighter than ever.

Gone are the feathers grey as ash.
Now it's flash of orange.
Dazzle of blue.
Flutter of yellow.
Definitely dazzle-eye magic in the sky.

Parrot turns green. Cousin Macaw turns
to scarlet.
Toucan gets a red beak and is proud of it.
Cock-of-the-Rock receives orange and likes
the fit.
Kiskadee is pretty happy with yellow.
Hummingbird keeps on saying "Do you like how
my feathers glow?"

Birds' Chorus: We happy to fly, happy to fly,
But we're happier still
Now we have colours to dazzle the eye
Colours to dazzle the eye.
Aren't we flying rainbows in the sky?
Aren't we flying rainbows in the sky?
Grey feathers goodbye.

Harpy: In case you're wondering about
Cormorant Queen,
well, since she had taken Watersnake's
greyish head,
she stayed the same as she was before.

Cormorant Queen: I am so overjoyed to be sitting once more
beside this stream so dear to my heart
that I am content to be as I am.
And let's be practical.
Bright colours may be fanciful, that I know,
but bright colours can also be easily seen
by a hunter with a gun or arrow.
No, diving deeply is enough for
Cormorant Queen.
My kingdom of water gives me enough
adventure.

*(Cormorant Queen does a ballet-like rendition of
diving.)*

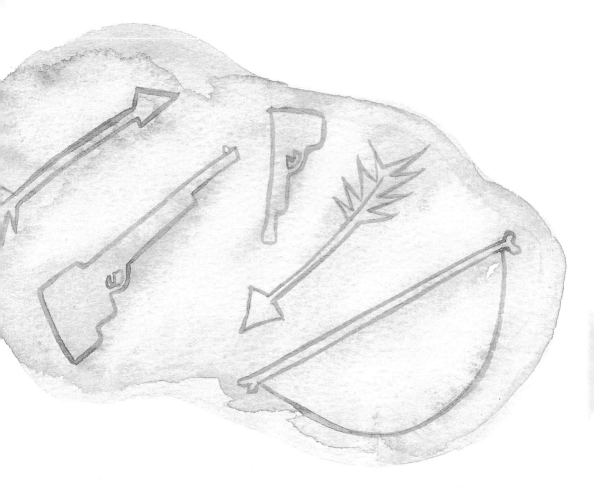

(To dramatic music, the shadowed silhouettes of hunters with guns and arrows appear. Birds flutter and dance all around the stage, almost in comic celebration of their new found colour. They can't see the hunters, who can be standing behind a sheet – or simply have footsteps suggested by drumming.)

Parrot: I'd rather be scarlet and green though easily seen.

Woodpecker: I'd rather have red and risk being dead.

Kiskadee: I'd rather be yellow and risk an arrow.

Birds' Chorus: We'd rather have feathers of the brightest
though hunters give us no rest.
We'd rather have more of colour, not less.

(Grey ghost of Watersnake re-enters. The birds cannot see him.)

Watersnake: *(With a hissing laugh, to the audience)*
Now those grey birds have feathers so bright
they have to fly for their lives
whenever hunters come into sight.
Heeeeee-heeeeee-heeeeeessssss.
Oh isn't it fun, isn't it fun
that they have to watch out for arrow and gun?
And just think, it's my fabulous skin
that caused all the confusion!
Heeeeee-heeeeee-heeeeeessssss.

(Exit Watersnake's hissing ghost.)

Harpy: Now, my feathered friends, you see what I meant
by the double face of colour.
For myself, I'm pleased to have less colour,
not more.
I'm proud of my crest and wings that soar
But as I gaze across the wide green of
the rainforest
on this long-ago beginning day
I can't help asking myself –
What does Rainbow think of grey?

Teachers' Notes

Choosing Parts

All the parts in this play will need confident readers, but the most demanding are those of Harpy Eagle, the Great Watersnake and Cormorant Queen.

Putting On the Play

You may wish to put on a performance of the play, rather than just reading it. The following suggestions may provide you with a starting point for your own ideas about staging a production. Obviously, the use you make of these suggestions will vary depending on the time and resources available to your school.

For permission to put on a profit-making performance of *The Great Snakeskin*, please contact the Editorial Department, Ginn & Co. Ltd, Prebendal House, Parson's Fee, Aylesbury, Bucks HP20 2QZ.
(There is no need to apply for permission if you are not charging an entrance fee, but please let us know if you are putting on any performance of this play, as we would be interested to hear about it.)

Staging

Clearly, with such an exotic and colourful story, the staging could be complicated and expensive. You can choose ideas to suit your purposes from the following suggestions.
Area
This play is full of movement and will therefore require quite a large floor area.
Background
Background scenery suggesting a tropical rain forest would be very useful in setting the scene. This could be painted on paper or card, but if you are feeling more adventurous you might like to consider the possibilities of camouflage netting, which can be borrowed from the Services or hired from Army Surplus stores.
Levels
You could set up areas at different levels for the birds to fly to and from. These could simply be chairs and tables, or you could use blocks, staging units or gymnastic equipment such as wall bars and horses. Safety should be borne in mind in the use and arrangement of these items.
The River
This can be suggested by the use of a sheet of blue or turquoise lightweight fabric of various shades. If you wanted to represent the river more authentically, you could use some silvery or even rusty-coloured satin fabric. This could be stretched across the stage and 'billowed' by offstage operators. Effects from ripples to storm-driven waves can be achieved by varying the strength and speed of the billowing.

Costumes

All the **birds** will need beaks. Simple card beaks over the forehead are easiest and do not hinder speech. **Toucan's** beak will need to be larger than the rest.
The **birds** can wear plain grey shirts and shorts or leggings, with grey cloaks. The cloaks just need to form a semicircle from wrist to wrist with arms outstretched, falling to the tops of the thighs. You could experiment with using skates or skateboards to help the birds 'fly' around the stage.
In the last scene, all the **birds** except

Harpy and Cormorant Queen will have to change into colourful cloaks. These could be made of crêpe or other colourful paper stuck, tacked or stapled on to cloth, or of scalloped brightly coloured cloth. For advice on colours, see the notes under each bird's name below.

The **Great Watersnake** will need a colourful costume that is detachable when the birds come to steal his skin. See the notes below.

Props

The only props necessary are a rope for Harpy and an arrow for Cormorant Queen. The arrow should be larger than lifesize and perfectly safe – perhaps made from cardboard.

Characters

These notes are just for guidance. The birds' natural colours, calls and movements have been simplified to make them easier to reproduce on stage. Of course, for most of the play the birds are entirely grey – they only have other colours right at the end.

The Great Watersnake

He is a mixture of all the brightly-coloured snakes of the rainforest. He could be played by a single person, but it might be more interesting to make the Watersnake more like a Chinese dragon, with several operators under a long 'skin'.

This skin will need to be detachable so that it can be carried off by the birds. Underneath, the operators should be dressed in grey.

The Watersnake will also need a detachable mask. This should be a head-dress which does not hinder speech.

Harpy Eagle

Plumage – grey.
Movement – sweeping, soaring and gliding.
Call – harsh yelping and screaming cries.

Cock of the Rock

Plumage – brilliant orange. He also has a large semicircular orange crest.
Movement – hopping, wild dancing
Call – squawking and cawing, and a low whistling noise made with wings.

Kiskadee

Plumage – yellow.
Movement – swift, darting flight.
Call – its raucous cry , which sounds like "kis-ka-dee", was interpreted by French settlers as "Qu'est-ce qu'il dit?" ("What does he say?").

Toucan

Plumage – yellow and red. Has an enormous brightly coloured orange, yellow and red beak with a black tip.
Movement – hopping on the ground, or undulating flight.
Call – loud croaks, barks and rattles.

Woodpecker

Plumage – red, cream and brown.
Movement – nervous, back-and-forth head movement.
Call – a tapping sound (may be made by tongue clicking).

Parrot

Plumage – scarlet and green.
Movement – shuffling walk, acrobatic flight.
Call – loud metallic screeches.

Owl

Plumage – brown and yellow.
Movement – swivelling head

movement, gliding flight.
Call – resonant hooting.

Hummingbird
Plumage – red, green and brown. Has a very long slim bill.
Movement – very fast, darting flight, but capable of hovering quite still.
Call – no voiced call, but makes a humming sound with wings.

Cormorant Queen
Plumage – dark grey or black.
Movement – diving, waddling, stretching, wing-flapping, long, sinuous neck movements. Graceful flight.
Call – grunting and throat-clicking.

The Hunters
The presence of the hunters at the end of the play can be suggested by drum-beats for footsteps. Alternatively they could be represented in the form of shadows. To do this, shine a bright light from behind the hunters on to a screen or sheet. A spotlight bulb in a desk lamp will suffice in a darkened room, but in brighter locations a 300-500 watt floodlight of the sort sold as security lights may be needed.

The hunters can be shadow puppets (with moveable arms and legs operated by strings if desired) or they could be performers. Placing performers or puppets near the screen will result in a sharp, normal-sized image; if they are further away, the image will be enlarged but fuzzy at the edges.